David Rowland

Autism Breakthrough

Discovery In Neurophysiology

LAP LAMBERT Academic Publishing

Imprint
Any brand names and product names mentioned in this book are subject to trademark, brand or patent protection and are trademarks or registered trademarks of their respective holders. The use of brand names, product names, common names, trade names, product descriptions etc. even without a particular marking in this work is in no way to be construed to mean that such names may be regarded as unrestricted in respect of trademark and brand protection legislation and could thus be used by anyone.

Cover image: www.ingimage.com

Publisher:
LAP LAMBERT Academic Publishing
is a trademark of
International Book Market Service Ltd., member of OmniScriptum Publishing Group
17 Meldrum Street, Beau Bassin 71504, Mauritius
Printed at: see last page
ISBN: 978-620-2-52232-8

Copyright © David Rowland
Copyright © 2020 International Book Market Service Ltd., member of OmniScriptum Publishing Group

Autism Breakthrough

Discovery in Neurophysiology

by **David Rowland**

Copyright © 2020 David Rowland

David Rowland

P.O. Box 30015, Prospect Plaza
Fredericton, NB E3B 0H8 Canada

Email: david222@hush.com

An Insider's View

Autism is simply a specialized way of thinking and interacting with the world. It is characterized by perpetual hyperfocus, intense mental concentration fixated on one thought pattern at a time to the exclusion of everything else, including one's own feelings.[6,17]

Autism, from the Greek word meaning *self*, was coined in 1911 by Swiss psychiatrist, Eugen Bleuler, who used it to describe withdrawal into one's inner world.[15] Autistic children appear to be in a world of their own, isolated and alone, with senses that can overload easily. These children talk endlessly about one subject, engage in repetitive behaviors (e.g., wringing hands, rocking the body), continually repeat certain words or phrases, and are resistant to change.[13]

Autism is more readily understood from the inside looking out. This is because those who are neurotypical (non-autistic) have no frame of reference with which to compare what they are seeing when they look in.

Autistic people have emotions but because of hyperfocus can only process those emotions intellectually, after the fact, by which time it is too late to have *felt* them. To the 99.6% or so of people who feel their emotions, it is incomprehensible that autistic people cannot. They observe how autistic people are emotionally aloof and socially awkward and presume that autism must be a disorder of some kind. Not so.

My case is an example of the above misunderstanding. In 1983, a psychiatrist at the University of Toronto diagnosed me as having a personality disorder. The correct diagnosis should have been Asperger syndrome (high functioning autism).   This psychiatrist mistook my autism for emotionally unstable personality disorder (EUPD), which is characterized by unstable relationships with others, an unstable sense of self, and unstable emotions.

Autism is currently considered to be a disorder, i.e., a pathological condition. It most definitely is not.   Autism is simply an inherent neurophysiological idiosyncrasy in how the brain processes information. Michelangelo, Mozart, Darwin, Jefferson, Edison, Tesla, and Einstein were autistic and can hardly be said to have been suffering from any kind of mental pathology.

Having an autistic brain is analogous to living 24/7 in an intellectual laboratory from which emotional and social distractions are prohibited from entering. For this reason, some, including climate activist Greta Thunberg, view their autism as a mental superpower.[14]

-   *David Rowland*

Contents

Epidemic of False Diagnoses

Autism Speaks reports that one in 59 children (1.7%) are diagnosed with autism spectrum disorder (ASD).[1] The oft-quoted figure during the 1960s was one in 2,500 (0.4%). A 420 percent increase suggests that autism may have reached epidemic proportions. Not so. The only epidemic is in false diagnoses of autism.

A 10-year Swedish study concluded that although the prevalence of the autism phenotype has remained stable, clinically diagnosed autism spectrum disorder has increased substantially.[2] A 2016 study reported that many children originally diagnosed with autism spectrum disorder were later found not to be autistic.[3] A 2019 comprehensive study in *JAMA Psychiatry* strongly suggests that autism is being significantly overdiagnosed.[3] Dr. Laurent Mottron, co-author of this most recent study, has expressed these concerns: "*The autism category has considerably overextended ...most neurogenetic and child psychiatry disorders that have only a loose resemblance with autism can now be labeled autistic ... you could not have ADHD and autism before 2013; now you can.*"[4] Doctors now tend to label as autistic anyone who simply has ADHD (or OCD) and poor socialization.

In 2013, the American Psychiatric Association merged the following four disorders under the umbrella of *autism spectrum disorder* (ASD): autism disorder, childhood disintegrative disorder, pervasive development disorder not otherwise specified (PDD-NOS), and Asperger syndrome. Autism now includes a spectrum of conditions of uncertain similarity. Professionals diagnose by ticking off symptoms on a checklist, without questioning the possible causes of said symptoms.

The symptom survey approach has been a major step backward in diagnosing autism, compared to the clinical phenotype diagnosing that was common during the 1960s. Phenotyping is based on observing gene expression in individuals and relating their conditions to hereditary factors.

The Spectrum Misconception

In 1980, DSM-III, the *Diagnostic and Statistical Manual of Mental Disorders*, defined autism as a "pervasive developmental disorder" characterized by a lack of interest in people, severe impairments in communication, and bizarre responses to the environment, all of which traits develop in the first 30 months of life.[5] This definition ignores the possibility or even likelihood that autism may be a congenital condition that only becomes apparent as the child develops.

In 2013, the DSM-5 introduced "autism spectrum disorder (ASD)" as an umbrella category under which are included a broad range of disorders that are characterized by (a) persistent impairment in reciprocal social communication and social interaction, (b) restricted, repetitive patterns of behavior, or (c) communicative disorders that include language and social impairments.[5] These criteria are so overly broad as to be meaningless for purposes of diagnosis.

This spectrum idea falsely implies that there can be different kinds or varying degrees of autism. Recent neurophysiological research clearly establishes that this is not so. There is only one autism and it is 100 percent. A person is either autistic or s/he is not.[6]

Autism does **not** even belong in the DSM-5 for the simple reason that it is **not** a disorder. Autism is simply an inherent neurophysiological idiosyncrasy in how the brain processes information.[6,17]

Implications for Research

Autism is neither a neurodevelopmental disorder nor a pathology. It is simply an inherent neurophysiological difference in how the brain processes information.[6,17] Because autism is inheritable, there must be a genetic weakness of some kind that is responsible for this neurophysiological anomaly. Unfortunately, research to date that attempts to pinpoint the specific DNA marker obscures rather than resolves the issue.[7,8,9,10] Research into genetic identifiers for autism cannot succeed if it falsely assumes that autism is a heterogeneous mixture of complex neurodevelopmental factors. Only if researchers isolate cases of true autism from the misleading spectrum can any headway be made in this direction.

Research into possible therapies is doomed to failure because autism is *not* a pathology. There is no biochemical agent and no behavioral modification technique that can alter how the autistic brain inherently functions.

The unique and defining characteristic of autism is hyperfocus, the perpetual and unrelenting state of intense single-minded concentration fixated on one thing at a time, to the exclusion of everything else, including one's own feelings.[7] The suspected cause of hyperfocus is dysfunction of the cingulate gyrus (CG), that part of the brain which focuses attention. Research now needs to direct its attention to discovering the factors that cause the CG to malfunction.

Autistic Traits Have a Common Cause

From intimate knowledge of how my own autistic brain functions, and from studying the behaviors of three autistic family members and seven other autistic people, I have compiled a list of 44 traits that all 11 of us have in common – as detailed in the following chapter. These traits appear to have a single cause: *hyperfocus*, the perpetual and unrelenting state of intense single-minded concentration fixated on one thought pattern at a time to the exclusion of everything else. Hyperfocus thus appears to be the unique and defining characteristic of autism that is responsible for all its observed traits.[6,17]

Hyperfocus keeps a person trapped in the mental/intellectual part of his mind with no ability to divide his attention between two thoughts (or stimuli), with the consequence that he never gets to **feel** his emotions. He can only process his emotions intellectually, after the fact. Without the ability to feel emotion, it is impossible to be spontaneous, to be emotionally available, to feel connected to others, or to be aware of how one is perceived. Anthony Hopkins spoke for every autistic person when he is reputed to have said, "*My whole life I have felt like an outsider.*"

Hyperfocus enables some visual people to see accurate, distinct pictures in exceptional detail and to manipulate these images in their heads. Michelangelo, Einstein, and Temple Grandin had/have this gift.

Hyperfocus enables some auditory people to compose music from melodies they hear in their heads. Mozart, Anthony Hopkins, and I had/have this gift.

Hyperfocus prevents a person from running two mental programs simultaneously. S/he takes everything you say literally because it is not possible to also simultaneously question how you use words. Similarly, an autistic person cannot also be picking up on subtleties or social cues. He cannot lie spontaneously because that would require dividing his attention between the truth and a falsehood.

Hyperfocus can be so intense that any sudden interruption (e.g., a door opening, an unexpected question, accidentally dropping something) shatters the thought pattern and can be experienced as anywhere from annoying to devastating. Loud noises instantly switch hyperfocus to the noise, which is then experienced with much more intensity than does someone with a neurotypical brain.

Meditation is impossible for someone trapped in hyperfocus because meditation requires letting go of focus. It is also unlikely that an autistic person can be hypnotized. Twice I tried but was unable to divide my attention between the instructions and the experience I was supposed to be having.

Autistic Hyperfocus

Hyperfocus is the unique and defining characteristic of autism that is responsible for all 44 of its observed traits listed below. Hyperfocus is the perpetual and unrelenting state of intense single-minded concentration fixated on one thought pattern at a time, to the exclusion of everything else.[6,17]

Approximately one-third of the traits listed below can also have other causes. This is why the symptom survey approach to diagnosing fails. Without understanding causality, the categorizing of symptoms creates only confusion.

Mental traits
- Hyperfocus: intense single-minded concentration
- trapped in thoughts
- mind always busy, tendency to overthink
- passionately pursues interests, often to extremes
- amasses encyclopedic knowledge about areas of interest
- self-awareness but no social awareness
- interruptions trigger agitation, confusion, or anxiety

Sensory overload
- hypersensitivity to noise and other sensory assaults
- experiences anxiety from being mentally trapped in noise/assault
- overwhelmed by overhearing unwanted conversations
- frequently overwhelmed by too much information
- coping with computers/electronics/forms may cause anxiety
- sensory overload makes it impossible to think or focus
- has difficulty listening to radio or talking with others while driving
- some autistic people may have a high threshold to physical pain

Emotional traits
- feels like an outsider
- unable to feel emotion

- may have physiological responses instead of emotion
- processes emotions intellectually
- anxiety bypasses the intellect to warn of unprocessed emotions
- incapable of experiencing fear
- can be angry without knowing so
- never (or rarely) cries or laughs
- cannot nurture self psychologically
- needs to shrink from displays of emotion by others

Social traits
- lacks innate motivation to socialize
- unaware of feelings, needs, and interests of others
- no awareness of how perceived by others
- unaware of socially appropriate responses
- doesn't get subtleties; unable to take hints
- unable to read body language
- no awareness of flirting

In conversation
- takes everything literally
- easier to monologue than dialogue
- oblivious to motivations of others while they are speaking
- doesn't pick up on sarcasm
- misses social cues and nonverbal communication
- participating in 3-way conversations may be overwhelming
- may have difficulty following topic changes

In relationships
- understands what love is but cannot feel love
- may understand empathy but not be able to feel it
- cannot be emotionally available to others
- others cannot provide an emotional safety net

Temperament
- innate forthrightness tends to scare others
- never bored, always engaged in some mental activity

- consistent to daily routines; agitated if the routine is disrupted
- spontaneity not possible; activities need to be pre-planned
- cannot lie spontaneously; can tell only premeditated lies

Neurophysiology of the Autistic Brain

Figure 1

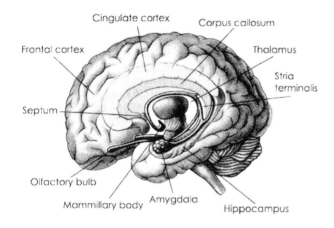

Cingulate Cortex/Gyrus	Left Frontal Cortex/Lobe	Right Frontal Cortex/Lobe	Amygdala
Dysfunctional	Dysregulated	Dysregulated	Inactive

The neurological structure of the autistic brain is the same as for every other brain. What is different about the autistic brain is how it functions with respect to its neurophysiology.

The **cingulate gyrus** (CG) is that part of the brain which focuses attention. Dysfunction of the CG is the suspected cause of hyperfocus, the perpetual state of intense single-minded concentration fixated on one thing at a time, to the exclusion of everything else. Hyperfocus is the unique and defining characteristic of autism.

The **amygdala** is the region of the brain which plays a central role in the expressing of emotions, especially fear. A dysfunctional **CG** prevents a person from feeling any emotion, with the result that the amygdala is virtually non-functioning. An autistic person typically never experiences fear.

The **left frontal lobe** is the intellectual, analytical, problem-solving part of the brain. The **right frontal lobe** is the emotional/creative processing part of the brain that plays a central role in spontaneity, social behavior, and nonverbal abilities. Some people are left-brain dominant while others are right brain dominant. Autistic people, however, are left brain exclusive.

The **CG** normally acts like an automatic transmission that seamlessly switches attention back and forth between the frontal lobes, as required. However, the dysfunctional CG in the autistic brain keeps the person permanently trapped in his/her left frontal lobe. Consequently, the autistic person can only process emotions intellectually.

The EEG neurofeedback I have done on the autistic brain reveals high alpha activity in both frontal lobes. In the neurotypical brain, however, alpha activity (8-12 Hz) is high only in the right frontal cortex, whereas the left frontal cortex reveals high beta activity (12.5-30 Hz). Dominant alpha frequencies in the autistic left brain are most probably compensating for the inability to access creativity and intuition from the right brain.

Neuropsychology of Autism

Table 1

	Autism	**ADHD**	**OCD**
Hyperfocus	hyperfocus[1]	fickle focus[2]	fickle focus[2]
Concentration	intense	intense	intense
Distraction	never distracted	easily distracted	self-distracts
Social Aspects	unable to understand and respond to social needs of others	poor social skills	may have social anxiety, fear of disapproval
Multitasking	unable to multitask	may be able to multitask	unable to multitask
Emotional Effects	Incapable of feeling emotion. Processes emotions intellectually.	Can trigger intense emotions.	Compulsive behaviors may be attempts to relieve emotional stress.

[1]**Hyperfocus** is defined as perpetual and unrelenting attention fixated on one thought or stimulus at a time, to the exclusion of everything else.

[2]**Fickle focus** is defined as intervals of intensely paying attention interspersed with episodes of distraction or impulsiveness.

The above chart compares the neuropsychology of autism to two conditions with which it is often confused: attention deficit hyperactivity disorder (ADHD) and obsessive-compulsive disorder (OCD). The confusing similarity between symptoms is what causes many cases of ADHD and OCD to be misdiagnosed as autism.

The two crucial differences with respect to autism are:
1. hyperfocus; and
2. processing emotions intellectually.

Differential Diagnosis

Differential diagnosis is distinguishing a specific condition from others that have similar clinical features. Based on similar behavior patterns, many with ADHD, OCD and even PTSD have been misdiagnosed as being autistic. However, the neurophysiological differences between autism and such other conditions can be profound.[6]

Both attention deficit hyperactivity disorder (ADHD) and obsessive-compulsive disorder (OCD) share a common trait, *fickle focus*, which is defined as intervals of intense mental fixation interspersed with episodes of distraction of impulsiveness. Fickle focus can look like hyperfocus that comes and goes; however, such is impossible because hyperfocus is perpetual and unrelenting. Autistic people never get any relief from their hyperfocus.

Because of the confusion between fickle focus and hyperfocus, many people with ADHD or OCD are misdiagnosed as being on the autism spectrum. Also, some who are truly autistic are given false multiple diagnoses that include either ADHD or OCD or both.

Table 2

	Autism	PTSD	ADHD	OCD
Hyperfocus	hyperfocus[1]	n/a	fickle focus[2]	fickle focus[2]
Cingulate Gyrus	dysfunctional	functional	functional	functional
Amygdala	inactive	hyperactive	active	hyperactive
Left Frontal Lobe	high alpha activity	high alpha activity	high beta activity	high beta activity

Neurochemical Imbalance	n/a	n/a	low dopamine suspected	low serotonin suspected
Social Aspects	unable to understand and respond to the needs of others	social skills unaffected by PTSD	poor social skills	social anxiety, fear of disapproval

[1]**Hyperfocus** is defined as perpetual and unrelenting attention fixated on one thought or stimulus at a time, to the exclusion of everything else.

[2]**Fickle focus** is defined as intervals of intensely paying attention interspersed with episodes of distraction or impulsiveness.

Autism appears to be entirely neurophysiological in origin. ADHD and OCD appear to be caused or aggravated by a biochemical imbalance of neurotransmitters. Low dopamine is suspected in ADHD and low serotonin suspected in OCD.

In both autism and post-traumatic stress disorder (PTSD), alpha frequencies predominate over beta in the left frontal lobe. In both cases, this phenomenon appears to substitute for being able to access alpha frequencies directly from the right frontal lobe. The difference is that in PTSD there is a psychological block to avoid remembering specific emotional events normally accessed from the right frontal lobe – whereas the autistic person is neurologically incapable of accessing anything from his right frontal lobe.

A further difference is that PTSD responds to therapy whereas autism does not. No amount of counseling or behavior modification therapy can talk an autistic person out of his/her hyperfocus.

Autism and Fear

Hyperfocus prevents autistic people from being able to *feel* emotions as they happen. They can only process their emotions intellectually, after the fact, a process that can often take 24 hours. By the time an emotion has been processed, it is too late to have been felt.

Nature has programmed into every human being an automated fear response that warns of perceived threats or impending danger. Autistic people appear to be the only ones who are incapable of experiencing this fear response. If you encounter someone who has never felt fear of any kind, this person is most probably locked into autistic hyperfocus.

In every risky, dangerous or life-threatening situation, the autistic person is always focused on the event itself and incapable of feeling fear or even nervousness in that moment. In my entire life, including 17 years of experience in martial arts, I never once felt fear of any kind. I have an autistic friend who says, "Fear is something that happens to other people."

Alex Honnold is the only person to have ascended the El Capitan vertical rock face in Yosemite National Park without the use of ropes.[11] Alex is a second generation autistic person who has never felt fear of any kind and whose amygdala is verifiably inactive.

Sometimes autistic people may intellectualize about fear, for example saying that after thinking about such-and-such decided it could be a scary thing. However, they are incapable of *feeling* fear.

Anxiety

Anxiety is different from fear. Fear causes an immediate adrenal *fight or flight* response that rapidly spikes one's pulse rate. With autistic anxiety there is no adrenal response.

Anxiety is experienced by the autistic person as an intuitive knowing that something is amiss – either that one's present course of action is going to end badly or that there are deep emotions that are being blocked from processing. In this sense, anxiety could be considered a safety net.

Whenever I feel anxiety, I stop, take a deep breath, and figure out which emotion is struggling to be acknowledged. Sometimes this involves deduction or running down a mental checklist. As soon as the emotion is named, the anxiety immediately stops.

Emotional Balance

It is extremely difficult, if not impossible, for an autistic person to live an emotionally balanced life. This is because the autistic brain is hard wired to be mental/intellectual without any ability to feel emotions as they happen. Autistic people can only process their emotions intellectually, after the fact, a process that can take 24 hours or so, by which time the opportunity to *feel* those emotions has long passed.

Fortunately, there are four ways to experience emotion that bypass the intellect. Autistic people gravitate towards these forms of expression in their pursuit of emotional balance:

1. *Instrumental Music.* Jefferson, Edison, and Einstein played the violin. Anthony Hopkins composes music from melodies he hears in his head. Mozart was the ultimate master of this gift.

2. *Art.* Michelangelo made his life's work the expression of emotion through his paintings and sculptures.

3. *Animals.* Autistic people feel connected to animals in a way that they are unable to feel toward other humans. Nikola Tesla shared his New York apartment with pigeons, whom he considered his only true friends.

4. *Sex.* During sex, the intellect is suspended for the purpose of feeling sensations and emotions spontaneously.

Redefining Autism

The symptom survey approach has been a major step backward in diagnosing autism compared to the clinical phenotype diagnosing that was common during the 1960s. Phenotyping is based on observing gene expression in individuals and relating their conditions to hereditary factors.

Environment plays no part in the causality of autism, which is an inherent neurophysiological anomaly in how the brain functions. A brain that is trapped in perpetual hyperfocus is incapable of responding to environmental or social pressures. Neither is it capable of responding to behavior modification therapy. No one can be talked out of autistic hyperfocus.

The Litmus Test

Hyperfocus is the unique and defining causal state of autism that creates its observed characteristics. Hyperfocus prevents someone from dividing attention between two thought patterns or two stimuli at the same time. An autistic person talking to you is incapable of feeling any emotion in that moment. The surest way to find out if someone is autistic is to ask these five questions, to which you will receive the following responses.[6,17]

Table 3

1.	I low often do you cry?	"*never*" or "*rarely*"
2.	How often do you laugh?	"*never*" or "*rarely*"
3.	What are you afraid of?	"*nothing*" or an intellectual answer
4.	What are you feeling now?	"*nothing*" or an intellectual answer
5.	Do you ever get bored?	"*never*"

Example of an intellectual answer:
"*No, I'm not angry. That wouldn't be logical.*"

Anyone who answers all five questions as above is autistic. Anyone who answers four or fewer as above is ***not*** autistic.

[**Note**: *If the person answers the third question with a phobia (e.g., of heights), then re-ask the question this way, "Aside from this phobia, do you normally experience fear of any kind?"*]

What the psychology professions now require is a causal based definition, for which I propose the following:[6,17]

Autism: Perpetual and unrelenting hyperfocus, the state of intense single-minded concentration fixated on one thing at a time, to the exclusion of everything else, including one's own feelings. Hyperfocus appears to be caused by a dysfunctional cingulate gyrus (CG), that part of the brain which focuses attention.

Intensity of Autism

The *autism spectrum* idea is counterproductive and needs to be scrapped. This erroneous concept has been the biggest contributor to the epidemic of false diagnoses of autism.

Autism diagnosis does **not** belong on any spectrum. There is only one kind of autism, not several. There are no shades of autism, nor any such thing as autistic tendencies. Autism is 100 percent. Either one is autistic, or s/he is not. There is no middle ground.

The only variable within autism is the intensity with which hyperfocus is experienced. Low functioning autistic people experience hyperfocus intensely. High functioning autistic people experience hyperfocus less intensely. If a visual model would be helpful, then it needs to be a vertical bar chart rising from greatest intensity (lowest functioning) to least intensity (highest functioning).

In my own family there are both extremes. One young lad was born with classic non-communicative autism. His younger brother was born with Asperger syndrome (i.e., high functioning autism). Clearly, it is the same genetic weakness that is responsible for both variations of the same autism.

Some autistic people also have dyslexia, and others not. There appears to be no hard data to suggest that dyslexia is more common among autistic people than it is in the general population.

Some autistic people avoid looking into people's faces and others hyperfocus on the face of the person to whom they are speaking. Many people appreciate the full attention they receive from this latter kind of conversation.

For some people with autism, words never make sense. Some never learn to speak and never come to understand the world as anything but one painful event after another.[13]

Some children with autism are prone to temper tantrums, simply because they are terribly frustrated and cannot tell anyone why. This is very different from children who have learned to use tantrums as a way of resolving emotional conflicts with others.

Non-communicative autistic children are the ones most intensely trapped in hyperfocus, and there is no known way to bring them out of it. An intensely autistic children cannot be taught to speak; however, some spontaneously start to speak on their own initiative, as Einstein did at age four.

The only non-communicative children who can be taught to speak are those who have developmental, learning, language, communication, or social disorders unrelated to autism.

The Futility of Therapy

Therapies for autism are aimed at socializing the child. It cannot be done. It is no more possible to socialize an autistic person than it would be to intellectualize a neurotypical person. The autistic brain inherently works in a precise way that cannot be changed. No one can be talked out of perpetual hyperfocus.

Applied Behavior Analysis (ABA) is the most common therapy that is attempted for autistic children. It is an intensive one-on-one program that aims to improve social skills by increasing desirable behaviors and decreasing problem behaviors. There is a vocal community of adults with autism, many of whom had ABA as children, who say that ABA is harmful because it is based on the cruel premise of trying to make people with autism "normal".[17]

Autism and Employment

Professor Stephen Shore has wisely stated, "If you've met one person with autism, you've met one person with autism."[18] Autistic people have a wide range of abilities and are employed as accountants, animal trainers, assembly line workers, automobile mechanics, bankers, carpenters, commercial artists, computer technicians, data analysts, draftsmen, engineers, equipment designers, inventory control technicians, journalists, laboratory technicians, library scientists, mathematicians, mortgage consultants, photographers, physicists, researchers, scientists, software designers, statisticians, teachers, telemarketers, veterinary technicians, web page designers, and welders.

There are no autistic politicians nor any autistic lawyers. This is because the autistic brain is hard wired for truth and integrity. It is not possible for an autistic person to divide attention between what needs to be done and what my political party orders me to do – nor between what is just and what my client has hired me to do. Counter arguments in both professions tend to obscure the truth and would overwhelm the autistic person with irrelevant details – plus autistic people are easily blindsided in debate by unexpected tactics.

The ideal career situation for an autistic person is to be self-employed, either in a fully functioning business of his/her own, or as a freelancer. This is because it is very stressful for an autistic person to know what needs to be done but to have a boss who prevents that from happening. Being second guessed or micromanaged is devastating to an autistic person.

If seeking employment from a business or institution is the only option, then I have the following tips to pass on to those who are about to have job interviews:

- Do your homework. Prior to the interview, learn everything you can about the organization and the opening it has;
- Be aware that the interviewer may be expecting social cues from you that you are unable to provide;
- Be aware that there may be times when you interpret literally something that the interviewer did not intend as such;
- Avoid the temptation to monologue. Give brief answers to questions and then pause to see what the next question is;
- As soon as you can comfortably do so, turn things around and start interviewing the interviewer. Ask questions about the organization, the job, what would be expected from you, etc. If you have any questions about the direction the organization is taking or difficulties it may be facing, tactfully ask about those also. The more interest you can show in the organization, the better.
- If you want the job, say so emphatically.

My Experience of Autism

Metaphorically, I have lived my entire life in an intellectual laboratory into which emotional and social distractions are prohibited from entering. My mind is a beautiful place in which to live. I enjoy finding answers to questions others may not have thought to ask. I become exhilarated every time I make a discovery that is new to me. Over the years, my intellectual laboratory has enabled me to acquire expertise in complementary medicine, neuropsychology, astrophysics, economics, business, music, and martial arts.

Autistic people are asocial by nature. For me this has been a blessing because social interactions would have been time wasters limiting what I have been able to achieve. For the most part, other people just get in the way of whatever I happen to be doing at any given time.

The essential characteristic of autism is hyperfocus: intense single-minded fixation on one thought pattern at a time, to the exclusion of everything else, including one's own feelings. We autistic people have deep emotions that we cannot *feel* in the moment they happen. We have to process our emotions intellectually, after the fact, a process that can take 24 hours or so, by which time the opportunity to feel that emotion has long passed. Because we cannot feel our own emotions, other people's emotions are a mystery to us.

Whenever there are unprocessed emotions needing attention, our brain lets us know by making us feel anxiety, a warning signal that bypasses the intellect. Whenever I feel anxiety, I run down a mental checklist of possible emotions; and as soon as I have identified the correct one, the anxiety immediately stops.

Hyperfocus prevents an autistic person from running two mental programs at the same time. Some specific examples of how this manifested in my life include the following:

- considering myself to be an *emotional flatliner* for never experiencing emotional highs or lows and facing everything with equanimity and a deadpan facial expression;
- always being calm and clear thinking in every emergency and crisis;
- never once experiencing fear of any kind, which made me a formidable opponent during my 17 years' experience in martial arts. In 1996, a test at the Auchenkyle clinic in Scotland indicated little to no activity in my amygdala (brain's fear center);
- having an affinity for animals, including dogs, cats, chipmunks, birds, deer – and especially a talking budgie who was my best friend for eight years.
- seeing everything in terms of black and white with never any shades of grey. A former employee once remarked that I make mud seem clear;
- never caring what others think of me;
- being a prolific writer of non-fiction who is unable to write fiction. My mind is incapable of fantasizing;
- feeling like an outsider, as if I were an extraterrestrial visitor observing the human species;
- taking everything literally, because I am incapable of running a second mental program questioning how people use words;
- intimidating others with my forthrightness. I am oblivious to how my words affect them;
- not being able to tap my foot in time with the music I am playing on the violin. If I give my attention to the timing, I lose the melody, and *vice-versa*. (Similarly, Temple Grandin has perfect pitch for singing but cannot feel the rhythm of the music[13]);

- being oblivious to social cues. I was considered the most clueless guy in grade 12 for being unaware that an attractive girl had been openly pursuing me;

- in high school and university, I befriended guys whose behavior I observed in hopes that I could learn how social interactions are supposed to work;

- knowing what love is but never actually feeling love. In university, I told a girl that I thought I loved her and was surprised at her non-response. Thinking was the only way I could know about love; but to her, if I had to think about it, it was not love;

- placing more importance on intellectual and recreational pursuits than on relationships;

- being incapable of emotional availability to my family;

- being unable to feel my emotions. Someone once asked in mid-conversation what I was feeling. I was not feeling anything and could not see the point of such a silly, irrelevant question;

- being overwhelmed by too many words or changes in topic during conversations. While I am tightly holding on to one thought waiting to respond to it, multiple other thoughts are fired at me, triggering anxiety;

- being impatient with small talk. My mind is always busy with projects of interest. It is not possible to divide my focus between thoughts of value and those that are meaningless to me;

- having a driven personality. I am always thinking or doing something. If I try to take a rest break, my mind is still be thinking about the task I just left and eagerly wishes to get back to it;

- being unable to work for anyone else. After 16 years of trying to fit into the corporate world, I realized that self-employment is the perfect match for my temperament;

- being overwhelmed by electronic technology, filling out forms, and lengthy passages in books;
- feeling pressure to finish one task completely before starting the next. Whenever someone asks me in mid-task to do something else, I insist on doing it right away, because it is not possible to divide my attention between two unfinished tasks;
- never being spontaneous. I have to pre-plan my activities;
- being unable to take a break from troubling work. Whenever I try to take a break, my mind is still fixated on the difficulty. I have to keep working at the problem until I resolve it; and
- being unable to listen to helpful advice while being overwrought with a task. My wife's suggestion to take a deep breath while telling me that everything is going to be OK is counterproductive, because I am unable to divide my attention between what I am doing and what she is saying.

Trauma Induced Autism

Until recent years, all my experiences and observations about autism supported the prevailing belief that autism is congenital. Although symptoms of autism may not become apparent for several years, the unique neurophysiological anomaly that is autism is most probably present at birth. This was the conclusion I had reached after studying 22 autistic people, including myself and three family members.

In 2015, trauma from a skull fracture and concussion intensified my lifelong autism. After that incident, lighting displays in stores triggered extreme anxiety, shopping became unbearable because of sensory overload from product displays and overheard conversations, interruptions to my train of thought caused anxiety lasting for hours, and the sound of a vacuum cleaner became excruciatingly painful inside my head. This effect is consistent with findings that patients with autism exhibit anxiety that is exacerbated in the setting of traumatic injury.[16]

In 2019, I began to wonder if trauma can exacerbate autism, could it also cause autism. While reviewing my notes, I noticed five case histories that were similar in that each person had suffered a single incident of extreme trauma. I was able to re-interview four of these people, and the evidence provided by so doing led me to conclude that in each case it was most probably the trauma that had induced the autism.[12]

At the time of re-examination in 2019, all four subjects were determined to have autism rather than post-traumatic stress disorder (PTSD). From their histories it was inferred that their brains would have been profiled as neurotypical if examined prior to their respective defining traumatic incidents. All four subjects passed with flying colors the Litmus test for hyperfocus, the unique and defining characteristic of autism.[6,17] All four had completely unemotional recall of the traumatic event in question, the exact opposite of how those with PTSD would have responded.

Subject A was born shortly after his father had been killed in a military accident. Subject A's family reported that until age five this child had been affectionate, socially interactive, and emotionally expressive. At age six, his mother married a man with a narcissistic personality disorder (NPD). From that point on, both parents neglected Subject A's emotional needs and frequently left him alone unsupervised.

Subject A remembers his failed attempt to commit suicide shortly before his seventh birthday. He wanted to end his unbearably painful life by joining his daddy in heaven – and almost succeeded. Clad in a makeshift military uniform and with a rope fashioned into a hangman's noose, the young lad had climbed to the top of his backyard fence and was about to scale the spikes sticking out of an adjacent telephone pole when a neighbor suddenly appeared and shamed him out of it. Subject A was thus not able to end his painful life; however, his trauma induced autism prevented him from ever again experiencing pain in his life.

Until he left home at age 16, Subject A was the victim of continuing psychological abuse that have his present family cringing in horror whenever he recounts one of those episodes. To him they were just things that happened about which he experienced no emotion, neither at the time nor in the telling of them afterward. He did not even realize that he had been abused.

Subject B showed me a photo of herself taken at age four, in which she was excitedly playing outdoors and simultaneously making a strong emotional connection with the photographer in a way that no autistic child could. Two years later all that changed. She never again felt excitement nor being emotionally connected to others.

At age 6, Subject B was forced to watch her drunken father threaten her mother at gunpoint. Her mother knew that her abusive husband would not pull the trigger if his daughter was watching. As an adult, Subject B has no social awareness and has difficulty figuring out other people's motivations. She pays more attention to her older son and cannot figure out why doing so upsets her younger son. If a friend gives her a hug, Subject B asks,"*Why are you doing that?*"

Subject B's hyperfocus has given her eidetic memory, which is of considerable benefit in her career as a technical support consultant and web designer. Hyperfocus also makes her impatient with people who keep repeating themselves in conversation. "*Why don't they remember what they say?*" she asks herself, not understanding that repetition is often for the purpose of emotionally connecting to the listener, to be able to feel that the speaker is being understood.

Subject C was outgoing and socially interactive as a child. As a teenager, his favorite activity was going to dances with his best friend. At age 18, Subject C witnessed this best friend being crushed to death in a mine collapse. From that moment on, he never again experienced emotional pain or pleasure. Whenever adversity struck his life, it was just something that happened about which he felt nothing.

Subject C's fearlessness made him a formidable opponent in the ring. For seven straight years he was a welterweight Golden Gloves boxing champion, never once having been knocked off his feet in all that time. Subject C has survived multiple strokes, multiple heart attacks, and multiple open-heart surgeries. When asked if he is afraid of dying, his response was, "*No. If it happens, I'm OK with that.*"

45

Subject D described himself as being an "overly loving kid". His sister verifies that until age four or five, Subject D was outgoing and emotionally expressive. His parents had been separated since his birth, and the only male role model in his home was his sister's husband, whom he worshipped and adored. He hung out with this adult brother-in-law, went fishing, played basketball and football, and was starting to learn a form of karate. All this came crashing down when the brother-in-law moved out of the house because his marriage had failed. Since that event, Subject D became withdrawn and angry at the world and has stayed that way until the present, at age 39. Since the day he lost the only person in his life who meant anything to him, Subject D has never felt any emotion, has never felt anything for anybody. He also has never felt fear and even laughed during two incidents in which he was threatened at gunpoint.

Subject D's hyperfocus has given him the same visual gift that Temple Grandin has, namely the ability to see accurate, distinct pictures in exceptional detail and to manipulate these images in his head.[13] He is obsessed with inventions, can look at anything and instantly see how to build something better.

None of the above subjects have ever experienced love or empathy. Subjects A and B have been able to figure out intellectually what these emotions mean, but the other three subjects have not. Subject C confided in me that one woman to him is the same as any other.

If autism can be induced by trauma in four individuals, then it is possible that trauma may cause autism in many others. However, four is an insignificant sample size from which to project meaningful information over the entire population of autistic people. We do not yet know if trauma induced autism (TIA) is rare or commonplace. More research is required and perhaps this can be accomplished by clinicians adding specific questions about trauma to their patient inquiries.

What is fascinating about these four cases is that they appear to be entirely psychosomatic in origin. Something so incredibly painful happened that these people somehow subconsciously changed how their brain functions so that they would never have to experience pain again. If such is the case, then perhaps there will one day be discovered a psychosomatic method to reverse TIA. Hypnosis is unlikely to work, because an autistic person cannot divide attention between the instructions and the experience s/he is supposed to be having. Psychotherapy is unlikely to work because a person whose brain is locked into hyperfocus cannot be talked out of it.

References

1. Autism Speaks: https://www.autismspeaks.org/autism-facts-and-figures.
2. Lundström, S., *et al*. "Autism phenotype versus registered diagnosis in Swedish children: prevalence trends over 10 years in general population samples." *British Med J* 350.1 (2015):h1961.
3. Blumberg, S.J., et al. "Diagnosis Lost: Differences between children who had and who currently have an autism spectrum diagnosis." *Autism* 20:7 (2016): 783-795.
4. Healthline.com: https://www.healthline.com/health-news/are-we-over-diagnosing-autism.
5. SpectrumNews: https://www.spectrumnews.org/news/evolution-autism-diagnosis-explained/.
6. Rowland, D. "Differential Diagnosis of Autism: A Causal Analysis", *J Neurol Neurophysiol* 2020 11:489.
7. Parishak Neelroop N, Swanup V, Belgard TG, Irmia M (2016) Genome-wide changes in lncRNA, splicing, and regional gene expression patterns in autism. *Nature 540*: 423-427
8. Siniscalco D, Kannan S, Sempruh-Hernandez N, Eshraghi A (2018) A stem cell therapy in autism: recent insights. *Stem Cells Cloning* 11:55-67.
9. Rylaarsdam L., Guemez-Gamboa S (2019) Genetic causes and modifiers of autism spectrum disorder. *Front Cell Neurosci* 13:385.
10. Grove J, Ripke S, Børglum AD (2019) Identification of common genetic risk variants for autism spectrum disorder. *Nat Genet* 2:431-444.
11. "Alexander Honnold", *Wikipedia*: https://en.wikipedia.org/wiki/Alex_Honnold.
12. Rowland, D. "Discovery of Trauma Induced Autism -Three Case Reports and their Review". *J Neurol Disord* 2020; 8:415.
13. Montgomery, S. *Temple Grandin*. New York, 2012: Houghton Mifflon Harcourt.
14. CBC News, Sept. 29, 2019. "How Greta Thumber's Autism Helps Give Her a Singular Focus": https://www.cbc.ca/news/world/how-greta-thunberg-s-autism-helps-give-her-a-singular-focus-1.5301634.
15. Blatt, G. "Autism", *Encyclopedia Britannica*: https://www.britannica.com/science/autism.
16. Radice-Neuman D., et al. "Overview of Impaired Facial Effect in Recognition in Persons with Traumatic Brain Injury". *Brain Injury* 2007; 21(8): 807-816.
17. Rowland, D. "A Need to Redefine Autism". *J Neurol Neurophysiol* 2020;8(2):143.
18. Devita-Raeburn, E. "The Controversy over Autism's Most Common Therapy", *Spectrum News*: https://www.spectrumnews.org/features/deep-dive/controversy-autisms-common-therapy.
19. "Stephen Shore", Wikipedia: https://en.wikipedia.org/wiki/Stephen_Shore_(professor).

About David Rowland

Member:
Canadian Association for Neuroscience

Editorial Board:
Scientific Journal of Technical and Biomedical Research

Publisher:
The Truth about Autism: *www.autism.info*

Author:
"Differential Diagnosis of Autism: A Causal Analysis"
Journal of Neurology & Neurophysiology 2020; 11:489

Author:
"Discovery of Trauma Induced Autism – Three Case Reports"
Journal of Neurological Disorders 2020; 8:415

Author:
"A Need to Redefine Autism"
Journal of Neurology & Neurophysiology 2020; 8(2):193

Printed in Great Britain
by Amazon